Xamb $1 R93

AMBER
VULTURECROCS

and other weird and wonderful African animals

*For Noah
and our family*

Contents

Ambervulturecrocs

Have you heard of the birds called the ambervulturecrocs?
They live in deepest Africa among the jagged rocks.

What do they feed on? What do they eat?
The droppings of blue monkeys and the toes of pygmies' feet.

And why are the vulturecrocs amber not green?
Why is it these creatures are so seldom seen?

'The reason they're amber we know is their diet,'
says vulturecrocologist, Wilberforce Wyatt.
'And by day they prefer to keep well out of sight,
so they chase the blue monkeys and pygmies by night.

'We suspect that the monkeys are bloated and blue
because they are frightened to go to the loo.
And since it's their toes that the vulturecrocs eat
the pygmies go round with thick socks on their feet.'

Jumpy Gecko-meleon

Jumpy gecko-meleon's a lovely colour green,
and though he's small he has the longest tongue
  you've ever seen.
So when he spots an insect that he thinks could
  taste quite nice
he shoots his tongue out, zaps it up and eats it in a trice.

BUT ...

The jumpy gecko-meleon is also easily scared,
so when he senses danger near, he gets himself prepared.
Up on his leafy perch he turns a different shade of green
to blend into the background, making sure he can't be seen.

This clever technicolor fellow can even change
  to brown or yellow!

NOW ...

A jumpy gecko-meleon that gets a sudden fright
is known to shed his tail as he is darting out of sight.
Then as a new one's forming – which will cause him
  growing pain –
he might go find the tail he dropped to stick it on again.

BUT …

Though this may sound quite simple, there's a most
   important catch –
the tail he finds has got to be a perfect colour match!
If it is brown and he is green, he *must* leave it *alone*
and carry on without a tail until the new one's grown.

Hare-brained Secretary Bird

The hare-brained secretary bird
is lucky she's employed,
she flies in late to work each day
and makes her boss annoyed.

He gives her strict instructions
about what she must get done,
but they just go in one long ear
and out the other one.

She settles down behind her desk
and when she's all alone,
she paints her claw nails shocking pink
and gossips on the phone.

With pencil stuck behind an ear
and specs perched on her beak –
you'd think she was intelligent
until you heard her speak.

She can't work the computer
'cos she's really such a dummy,
except to play the simple games
like mind-sweeper and rummy.

And every day she brings to work
a bag of snakes to munch
but still hops off at half past twelve
to have an early lunch.

She's not a bit attractive –
nothing much to be admired,
which makes one really wonder
why this bird has not been fired.

Rambaboon

The huge and hairy rambaboon
makes all the females sigh and swoon.
They flock around him just like sheep
and think of him when they can't sleep.

Jealous – the apes and chimpanzees
do everything they can to please
their lovesick ape and chimpy mates –
they bring them fruit and nuts and dates.

But no, when rambaboon's around,
all big and strong and muscle-bound,
those chaps see at a single glance
they simply do not
    stand a chance.

Monkeystrich

A monkeystrich will lay her eggs
while standing upright on three legs.
It's lucky if on sand she's standing
'cos then they'll have a nice, soft landing.
But if she drops them on the rocks
her chicks will suffer awful shocks.

So monkeystrich dad takes great care,
and when there's danger shouts, 'Beware!
Please move on to some nice, soft earth
and give our kids a safer birth.'

Zebrapedes

Zebrapedes are weird indeed
and very seldom found.
In their black and white pyjama stripes
they crawl down on the ground.

They have a hundred little feet
to help them move along,
and if they spy a friendly face
they like to sing a song.

Then sometimes – if they're in the mood –
there's also a good chance
they'll get in line and kick their feet
and do their special dance.

You'd think they were performing
in some fancy Broadway show,
singing and dancing on a stage
down on the ground below.

So if you spot some zebrapedes
you know what you should do –
just clap your hands and shout 'Encore!'
and they'll perform for you.

Dolphinduck

On a very clear day – if you look out to sea
you might have a real stroke of luck,
for frolicking happily out in the waves
you could spot a dolphinduck.

This very large fish – which is also a bird –
has a duckbill and little duck legs
but gives birth to her babies in water, because
she's a mammal and cannot lay eggs.

These cute little dolph-lings have tiny webbed feet
to help them to paddle around,
but their whole lives they'll never get out of the sea
to waddle like ducks on the ground.

Their dolphindrake dad takes them daily to school
where they learn how to swim when it rains,
how to exercise somersaults, catch the right fish
and to build up their dolphinduck brains.

Dolphinducks are real clever, as everyone knows,
they're the brainiest fish in the sea,
but they're also good-natured and loving and kind
as each one of us humans should be.

Brawny-tawny-buffalion

Deep in the wilds of Africa
where animals roam free,
don't be surprised if you will find
some hiding up a tree.

It's not the hunters that they fear
though there are lots around,
it's the brawny-tawny-buffalion
prowling on the ground.

He does this when he's hungry
and he wants to make a kill,
so he stalks his prey both night and day
until he's had his fill.

And when he's finished eating
and does *not* want any more,
he rubs his horns and shakes his mane
and gives a mighty roar.

Then, once he's settled down to snooze
beneath a leafy tree,
the animals come out and shout
'All clear! Hooray! We're free!'

Squirrelfox

In forests, parks or avenues, wherever oak trees grow
you're sure to see a squirrelfox scampering to and fro.

He hardly *ever* stands still – he's for*ever* rushing round,
with bushy tail flying behind or trailing on the ground.

Some people think this restlessness is just because he's shy,
but that's not really true – there are a few good reasons why.

In spring and summer squirrelfox works very hard indeed
collecting acorns, seeds and nuts – his family to feed
throughout the winter, when they all go into hibernation –
a job he does with energy and lots of concentration.

Or like some other bush-tails who've turned into
  nervous wrecks
it could be that he's suffering from 'squirrelfox complex'.
For they imagine that they're being chased by
  panting hounds –
and so they keep their foxy ears alert for threat'ning sounds.

And if they hear the faintest 'woof' – or if a dog they see,
they take off in an instant up the very nearest tree.

Now isn't that a funny joke –
dogs barking underneath an oak,
while nibbling acorns, squirrelfox,
safe on a branch, looks down and mocks,
with a sly smile which seems to say,
'Poor chaps, you've missed again today.'

Fleagle

The fleagle is a jumpy bird who's sometimes agitated
like after she has laid her eggs, when she must be sedated.
At night she's given calming pills to help her feel
  more restful
so she won't jump and crack her eggs – there's usually
  a nestful.

Sometimes the daddy fleagle likes to take over the sitting,
allowing mommy fleagle to get on with all her knitting,
for when the baby fleagles hatch they usually feel cold
and need to wear small jumpers till they're three or
  four days old.

As soon as they are strong enough they spring out
  of their nest
and if they land upon their legs, they've passed
  the fleagle test.
A second jump they have to do
  attached to some elastic
like mini-bungyjumpers they
  zoom down ... and up ... *Fantastic!*

The parent fleagles beam with pride to see their
   offspring spring,
and give each other itchy bites, but not the ones that sting –
not bites that make red bumps come out which make
   you scratch like mad
but bites of love exchanged between a fleagle mom and dad.

Pantherprawn

From the moment that he's born
the beady-eyed black pantherprawn
knows that it could well be his fate
to end up on a dinner plate
with chips or rice – a tasty dish …
or maybe swallowed by a fish.

So stealthily along the sandy ocean floor he creeps
his beady prawn eyes open wide – he never ever sleeps …

Just travels in and out the rocks
with feelers out to ward off shocks,
his body and ten legs as well
protected by a crusty shell,
his long black tail, sharp as a whip
with panther claws along the tip.

This pop-eyed prawn is so well armed
you'd think he never could be harmed,
that a tough creature of this sort
could never end up being caught.

Yes, it is hard to understand
how pantherprawns land up … on land.
But when on menus they appear
we *now* know why they are so dear.

Albatrossaurus

How unfortunate for us
that albatrossaurus
are nowhere on earth to be found!
Of course one may see 'em
in some science museum
but never alive on the ground.

Research has revealed
they were massive in size
and their bodies so brilliantly white,
that they could be spotted from thousands of miles
in the daytime and specially by night.

Skeletons show these huge dinosaur monsters
were birdlike, with beaks, wings and legs,
and although it's amazingly hard to believe,
it's been proved they were hatched out of eggs.

Since for millions of years they were on earth before us ...
we don't know much more about albatrossaurus.

Octohorse

Octohorse moves very fast,
but only when he trots,
'cos when he tries to gallop
he gets all tied up in knots.

He has eight legs with hooves, you see
and when he picks up speed,
they kick into each other
which hurts very much indeed.

And then they get entangled
forcing Octohorse to trip –
or if it's rainy weather
and the ground is wet – to slip.

He falls down flat upon the ground,
which is extremely sore,
and while he lies in pain, groans, 'I
won't gallop any more.'

But when he's feeling better
he forgets, as we all do.
So now you know why Octohorse
is always black and blue.

Warthog-goat

Warthog-goat is not handsome or pretty,
in fact, he's exceedingly gross.
He also gives off a most horrible smell,
as you'd find if you had to get close.

His eyes are all dopey and droopy,
he has two pairs of tusks that curl out,
with a face that is warty and whiskered
and a goat-beard and long pig-like snout.

His body's quite tough, but top heavy,
on his back there's a long hairy mane,
with four short skinny legs to support him
as he wanders all over the plain.

But while warthog-goat does seem repulsive,
his nature's good-humoured and sweet
and his smile simply dazzles and lights up his face
when he finds something tasty to eat.

Leopardeer

Do not go near a leopardeer,
he'll eat you up for dinner,
as no matter who he fights with
he will always be the winner.
Do not be fooled by his cute face,
his nature's very fierce,
so if you see him – as I said –
just make yourself real scarce.

The female, leopardess-deer, is
a very different beast.
She'd never ever
   think of
making me or you
   her feast.
The thing is, you
   can't take a chance
and venture near to see
whether the one in front of you
is a HE … or is a SHE!

Nyala-impala

Nyala-impala is not at all well,
he's looking decidedly blue.
He doesn't have chicken pox, measles or mumps
so it must be a dose of the flu.

His horns are red-hot and his tail's drooping down
and the hair on his back has gone frizzy.
With no interest to eat the long grass at his feet
he just stumbles along feeling dizzy.
He wobbles his way to the watering hole
and sticks his whole head in the pool,
swallows water in gulps, which right away helps
to refresh him and make him feel cool.

Then after a nap in
   the shade of a tree
he begins to feel
   perky again.
So he stretches his legs
   and with spring in his step
he goes bounding all
   over the plain.

Bee-squito

The bee-squito is sometimes glum
and not at all amused.
He doesn't want to buzz or hum
because he's all confused.

He cannot work out whether he
is a mosquito or a bee.

By day on wings he loves to fly
and stings whoever should come by,
but then he also flies by night
and looks for people he can bite.

He's all mixed up and in a tizz
Can't work out what he really is.

He knows he's not a butterfly … or moth or gnat or flea,
'I guess I'm half mosquito and the other half a bee.
And whether it's by day or night
I scare off everyone in sight.'

Indeed, those living in the area
are frightened they will catch beelaria.
So to be sure that they do not
they rush to get a vaccine shot.

Once they know they can't be harmed
They don't feel in the least alarmed,
and if they hear a buzz or hum,
they laugh, 'Let that beesquito come!'

Beesquito doesn't mind at all.
He knows it's simply nature's call
that makes him want to sting and bite –
a force too strong for him to fight,
and he can't feel ashamed or sad
because he really is not bad.

Rhinorat

Rhinorat is very fat,
he really loves his food,
and for a feast this greedy beast is always in the mood.

He doesn't like it when his friends refer to him as 'Fatty'.
In fact it makes him so annoyed he gets quite rhinoratty.

'I'm looking great,' he boasts to them,
'I have a perfect figure,'
and doesn't seem to notice when they smile or when
   they snigger.

He eats five big meals every day
and five more every night,
with snacks to gnaw and nibble on when he feels like a bite.

His rhinohorn is there to warn him when he's overfed
it honks and hoots and blares and toots
and goes a cherry red.

Then rhinorat knows that is that – the eating has to stop
for if he doesn't, sure as eggs, he'll definitely pop.

But if you even *dare* suggest that he should go on diet
he'll twitch his whiskers, twist his tail and start a rhino-riot.

Bunnybearbug

Would you like to hug
a bunnybearbug?
He'll keep you warm, he'll keep you snug.
You'll find him useful when it snows
but never touch him on the nose.
You see, that makes him most upset
because he likes to keep it wet.
But if you stroke his hairy ears
his eyes will fill with joyful tears
and he will kiss you
   on the cheek
and make a bunnybearbug
   squeak.
A happy fellow
   he will be
if you will treat
   him lovingly.

Pollypiggle

If you like to have a giggle
look out for a pollypiggle –
a bright red bird with snouty beak –
you'll be amazed to hear him speak.

'Ello! Ello!' he keeps repeating
(but not when sleeping or when eating)
while fixing you with birdy eyes
to see if you express surprise.

And if you answer, 'Hello Polly!'
he smiles right back and squeaks 'Good Golly!'
and makes a sort of 'oink' to show
that he's a piggy down below,
then gives his curly tail a wiggle
and screeches, 'I'm a pollypiggle!'

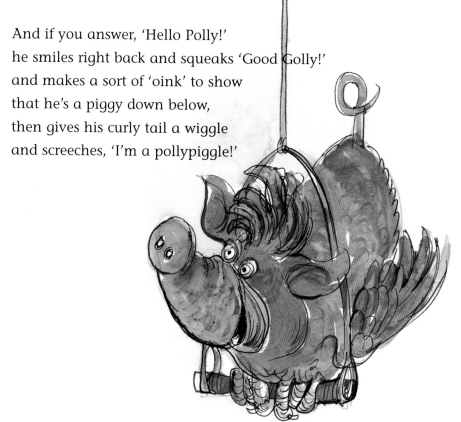

Twenty-three-humped camelbat

In the African desert
where there's no one around
'cos the sand is so hot
and no water is found,
if you fly in a plane
and look down from the sky,
just maybe you'll see a strange creature pass by.

A camel by day, he tramps over the sand,
while by night on batwings he takes off from the land.

The twenty-three-humped camelbat,
no bumpier beast you'll find than that.

He isn't comf'table to ride
or walk the steaming sand beside,
but you can have a lot of fun
after the setting of the sun.
Just hold on to his wings and fly
way up into the desert sky.

If an oasis you should see
beneath the shade of a palm tree,
tug on a wing to make a stop
and camelbat will let you drop.
But he'll make sure that you will land
quite safely on that desert sand.

What an adventure that will be
on camel-humped-bat twenty-three!

Hippo-chondri-ant

Hippo-chondri-ant always complains that he's not well
but looks so strong and healthy, you would never ever tell.
He wallows in the mud pools as he's always done before,
but all the time complains that every part of him is sore.

He says his blood pressure is high
his head aches so he wants to cry
his throat is sore
he sweats a lot
his nose is blocked
his nerves are shot
his stomach cramps
he's all in knots
and now his skin's
covered in spots
he suffers heartburn
in his chest
his legs pain so
he gets no rest
at night – no not a wink of sleep
just lies there counting goats and sheep.

He keeps a stock of medicine and every kind of pill
he gets from Hippo-doctor up on top of Hippo-hill.
His brothers and his sisters seem to suffer ill health too
'cos every day they're at the doctor standing in the queue.

Says doc, 'There's nothing I can find.
I'm sure that it's all in the mind.
Don't swallow all that medicine.
Get smart and throw it in the bin.'

Bullyphant

A bullyphant has a long trunk
two ears and one large horn.
They say he also has two tusks
when he is newly born.

These fall off when he's still a cub
just like your baby teeth,
except that once they're out and gone
no more grow underneath.

When he gets cross, the bullyphant
roars loudly and goes red,
which scares the baby monkeys so –
they sometimes wet their bed.

A bully ... bullyphant is not.
It's simply that his temper's hot.

It's something he just can't control,
he even stomps his feet,
but when his crossness disappears
he's really very sweet.

Bushbabybok

Bushbabybok have a spring in their step
as they prance in the grassland and veld,
with their crybaby eyes open wide in surprise
they're so cute they can make your heart melt.

In the branches of gumtrees they live when they're small,
sleeping peacefully all through the day,
but once they've awakened and eaten their supper,
they stay up the whole night and play.

SHE bushbabybok leaps amazingly far
when she's growing, although she stays small,
while the long-legged *HE*, who can jump very high,
has large antlers and grows rather tall.

When *much* later on, *HE* and *SHE* fall in love
and go out on a date for the night,
the animals who haven't *yet* gone to bed
smile and giggle at this funny sight.

The *HE* is so tall while the *SHE* is so short
and they move at so different a pace,
with the one springing high and the other one far
they just can't ever meet in one place.

But each time that they pass they let out a short cry
and their bushbabybok-eyes they wink,
which is their way of saying 'I love you my dear –
never mind what those gigglers may think!'

Tortiskunk

A tortiskunk is full of spunk
as everyone knows well,
and yet he cannot keep a friend,
the reason is his smell.
His odour is so bad, you see –
no one will keep him company.

No pig? No elephant? No horse?
Another tortiskunk? ...
Of course!
Even a monkey I suppose,
but with a peg upon his nose.

But tortiskunk is not upset,
he takes it very well,
and when he sees someone approach,
he dives into his shell.

Then, when he thinks the coast is clear
and no one can complain,
because he also needs fresh air
he pops out once again.

'I can't stay in my shell all day,
it's far too claustrophobic.
I also need to exercise –
both stretching and aerobic.'

Still when it's time to go to sleep
this tortiskunk knows well,
the only place for him
is on his bunk inside his shell.

Mousie-brownowl

And then there's the mousie-brownowl,
a really unusual fowl.
His face is all round, but his eyes are quite square,
he makes a 'whooo' sound as he flies through the air,
like a lonely old wolf on the prowl.

What makes him so strange you'll agree
is that mousie-brownowl loves TV.
From soapies to news he
is not really choosy,
as long as there's something to see.

So at night-time when everyone sleeps,
he flies round the houses and peeps,
and if he should see
in a lounge a TV,
through the window he instantly leaps.

Right away he will switch on the set
and press buttons until he will get
a show or a movie
that he thinks is groovy,
or one that he hasn't seen yet.

What makes his enjoyment complete
is to have something tasty to eat,
something cheesy to munch
or some peanuts to crunch
or a cracker that must be wholewheat.

A secret we now need to share
is why mousie-brownowl's eyes are square.
It seems that they've been
so long glued to the screen
that the roundness is no longer there.

Kudu-gnu

What do you think that you would do
if you were born a kudu-gnu?
How ever do you think you'd cope
up on some rocky mountain slope – with all the
  other antelope?

For just like all those other deer,
a kudu-gnu has lots to fear,
because there's always danger near.

The cheetahs and the mountain lions, spotted leopards too
are always on the look out for a juicy kudu-gnu.
And game-hunters in four-by-fours with rifles in their packs,
aiming to bag a kudu-gnu, will follow in his tracks.

Perhaps you think a kudu-gnu
would be much safer in a zoo!
Well, let me tell you, that's not true.

His spiral horns look after him whenever danger lurks,
a special radar system – it's amazing how it works!
They light up red, and flash and twirl and make a
  hooting sound,
which scares off all his enemies for miles and miles around.

So kudu-gnu is never scared, but ever free to roam
the mountain slopes and rolling plains where he has
  made his home.

Blue-spotted Guineafowldove

The Blue-spotted guineafowldove
will coo loudly when he is in love.
In a treetop he'll wait
for his pink-spotted mate
till the stars twinkle brightly above.

When she joins him she gives a shy squeak
and asks for a kiss on the cheek,
but he gives her a peck
on her pink-spotted neck
with the tip of his sharp little beak.

'Now dearest', she cries, 'that was sore.
Your aim is decidedly poor.
If you kiss me again
and you give me a pain
I don't think that I'll want any more.'

'I am sorry', my dearest says he,
'but I nearly fell right off the tree,
which caused me to miss
when I gave you the kiss,
I was thrown off my balance you see.'

Then together they fly to the ground
and when a good spot they have found,
they cuddle and coo
the entire night through
driving everyone mad with the sound.

Porcu-gorill

If you should meet a porcu-gorill, you must not move
  an inch
'cos if he jabs you with his quill, the pain will make
  you flinch.

And make sure that you never stare or shout out
  'Gee!' or 'Crikey!'
because his massive body is all prickily and spikey.

From head to toe, you'll see that he is covered in
  sharp quills,
which look like massive toothpicks to clean teeth
  with after meals.

When he stomps through the jungle paths, his quills
  jangle and clatter,
which frightens all the animals and makes them dart
  and scatter.

But though he's such a scary beast he isn't brave at all,
for when he senses danger's near he curls up in a ball.

Like a huge rock he slowly rolls along the sandy ground
until he's absolutely sure that he is safe and sound.

Then he unfolds and makes himself gorillish once again
and thumps his chest – jabbing his paws – which makes
  him roar with pain.

What a silly porcu-gorilly!

Sharkitty

A sharkitty cannot be found
up in the air or on the ground,
but only in the deep blue ocean
swimming with the strangest motion.

Humungus jaws he opens wide
and sways his tails from side to side.
With rows of teeth so sharp and white
he gnashes out at all in sight,
and with a smile so cruel and vicious
swallows all the smaller fishes.

His kitty whiskers too are fierce
and sharply pointed, so they pierce
whatever happens to swim by,
which hurts it so it starts to cry.

Indeed there cannot ever be
a fish more scary in the sea.

So ... if you're in deep water and you hear a
    meeow-like screech,
stop – turn around – and very quickly head
    back for the beach!

Flamingoose (pronounced 'Flay-mingoose')

Flamingoose is famous
for her lovely, glowing face,
her gorgeous rose pink feathers
and her elegance and grace.

In the birdie beauty contests
she wins all the 'golden eggs'
as she wows the wide-eyed judges
with her long and shapely legs.

Her mate, the flamingander,
is a charming, handsome bird
with feathers a light turquoise blue
just very slightly furred.

When newborn, flamingoslings
are quite bald, with flat, webbed feet,
but they very soon grow feathers
and turn out to be real neat.

Now while flamingeese have glamour,
when it comes to brains they've naught.
All that beauty is but skin deep,
in their minds there's not a thought.

Rock-cobra Dassie

The rock-cobra dassie
is not very fussy
except when it comes to his food.
He will never eat meat or touch anything sweet,
as it causes a change in his mood.

In fact we've discovered that most anything
can set him off into a total mood swing.

When he feels like a dassie
there's nothing to fear,
he just plays in the rocks,
full of fun and good cheer.

But when cobra takes over
he's quick to attack,
so the best thing to do
is to show him your back!

With his fangs filled with poison he raises his head
and whatever he spits at … is sure to drop dead!

But suddenly,
just like a pot off the boil
he'll draw in his fangs
and slump down in a coil.

And in a deep sleep in the sun he will snore,
till he wakes to become a sweet dassie once more.

Chimparaffe

Chimparaffe will make you laugh, he's such a funny fellow,
with brown and furry chimpy ears and neck so long
   and yellow.
Because he is so tall his head keeps bumping into trees,
and then the leaves tickle his nose – so that he has to sneeze.

He bends his neck down to the ground, then straightens
   like a stick
and sprays out a great big 'KERCHOO!' because he's aller-gic.
'Bless you!' his chimparaffe kids shout, 'Mom, bring a
   big flat leaf
to wipe our Daddy's nose and face and give him some relief.'

'He needs an antihistamine, his allergy to treat.'
So off Mom swings to Jungledoc just two trees down
   the street.
'Just give him this blue pill,' says Jungledoc, 'and then
   it oughter
clear up his nasal passages – he must swallow it with water.'

Then, once the pill has worked and chimparaffe has
   ceased to sneeze,
he smiles, 'I promise from now on I'll keep well clear
   of trees.'

Hyenacow

Hyenacow is never blue
despite the fact that she can't moo.
She smiles a lot and loves to laugh,
especially when she feeds her calf.
'Ha-ha! Ho-ho! Haw-haw! Hee-hee!'
she rocks and rolls delightedly.
She chortles and she chuckles,
and she tinkles and she titters,
till hyenabull says, 'Cool it!
You are giving me the jitters.'
But hyenacalf is not disturbed
he doesn't seem to bother,
just sips on, grinning, 'No one makes
a milkshake like my mother.'

Meercaterpellar

An exceedingly popular fella
is the tan-coloured meercaterpellar.
He thinks it's great fun to sit out in the sun
but not ever beneath an umbrella.

He will tan all day long with his friends
as the sun in the heavens ascends,
till his meercaterskin gets all wrinkled and thin
and begins to curl up at the ends.

As he gradually starts to change shape,
getting shrivelled and dry like a grape
turning into a raisin – it's really amazin'
(you should see it on videotape!).

Then says he, 'I've had quite enough heat.
In the morning again chaps we'll meet.
I really can't stay so it's 'Cheers!' for today,'
and he crawls home on caterpell'feet.

Chief Bluebottle Wildebeest

Chief Bluebottle Wildebeest, as you'd suppose
has a sting in his tail and a blue bottlenose.
He roams with his herds on the grasslands and plains
where the grazing is good, specially after the rains.

Of course there are problems he has to sort out,
The one's mountain lions ... the other is drought.
For when lions get hungry and hunt things to eat,
there is nothing more tasty than wildebeest meat.

But ... when danger is lurking, Chief's bluebottle nose
lights up in a flash and it sparkles and glows,
and his stinging tail's ready to whip and to whack
any lion or hyena that dares to attack.

It's in the dry season, when there's no more rain,
that his bottlenose comes to the rescue again.
He bends down and pushes it deep in the sand
and it instantly smells where there's well-watered land.

Then he blasts on his horn to the herds all around,
who muster in thousands on hearing the sound,
and pushing and shoving they follow his lead
as they thunder down south in their yearly stampede.

Days and nights they charge on, across valley and plain,
till they finally come to green pastures again.
But … too tired to graze, they just flop to the ground
in a state of exhaustion – and the *only* sound
that they make, as they lie, almost breathless from cramp –
is the grunt,
'Ghrrr … Chief Bluebottle – Ghrrr … is the champ!'

Penguinroo

Penguinroo is rather new,
he came from far away,
but when he saw our lovely shores,
he said, 'I'm going to stay.'

He called his friends and family
and set up a fine colony,
which everybody came to see
and wonder what this 'THING' could be.

'It really cannot be a bird,
it's got no wings – just flippers.
It's black and white and slightly furred
with feet that look like slippers.

'Look how it waddles on the sand,
its flippers on its rumps,
and when it needs to leave the ground
it doesn't fly – it jumps!

'It's out the water much too long,
a fish it cannot be.
And yet it didn't come by boat
but swam in from the sea.

'And look – its mate is just the same,
but it must be the mummy
because it keeps its babies
in a pocket on its tummy.'

Swallow-whale

The swallow-whale has problems
there's a simple reason why,
one part of him just wants to swim,
the other part to fly.

In water, though he's huge and fat,
he moves along with ease,
but now and then he floats up top
to catch the fresh sea breeze.

'Ah what a lovely day,' he sighs,
'I think I'll take a shower,'
 and shoots water through his blow-hole
with amazing bursts of power.

Then his feathered wings start flutt'ring
as he feels the urge to fly
and the fishes hear him mutt'ring,
'I have got to have a try.'

Like propellers on a sea plane
swallow-whale's wings start to turn,
and they keep on going faster
while his heart is in a churn.

But the truth is he's too heavy
for a lift off to the sky,
he just sinks down in the water
with a very doleful cry.

So it seems that swallow-whale is just too big to be a bird
and to think that he could ever fly is totally absurd.

Lamb-maltese poodle

The lamb-maltese poodle's a wonderful pet,
a fluffy white cottonwool ball.
He barks when he's happy and bleats when upset
and comes running whenever you call.

You might call him Monty or Maxie or Cuddles,
this baby you love and adore,
and you never get cross when he makes wee-wee puddles
on the rug on the diningroom floor.

He's fussy with food,
from a tin he won't eat,
loves home-roasted chicken,
but will not touch meat.
At times he will graze
on the grass on the lawn
as little lambs do
quite soon after they're born.
And if he sniffs chocolate …
he's under your feet,
so you give him a small piece
but, just for a treat!

So it seems that he's gotten … spoilt rotten!

Like Mary, wherever you go your lamb follows,
and at night when you're lying in bed
he jumps up and cuddles so closely beside you
that sometimes he lands on your head.

He gets most distressed when you wear sheep-skin slippers!
so you just have to give them away
'cos to make sure your lamb-maltese poodle is happy
you feel it's a small price to pay.

And that's why he's gotten ... spoilt rotten!

Greyhound-cheetah

At the Animal Olympic Games
you'll find some very famous names.
And those who can't get there to see
will watch the action on TV.

Swimmers, fliers, runners, jumpers
come from near and far
to try to win the medals –
but there's one real *SUPERSTAR*.

The fastest animal on land,
the brilliant greyhound-cheetah.
With 99 gold medals
he's the champion record beater.

He runs and jumps and hurdles
like a bullet on the track,
and whatever race he enters
he is sure to beat the pack.

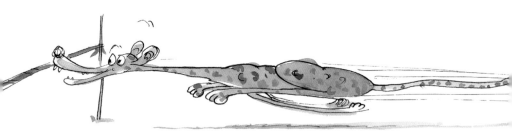

'Hooray for Greyhound-cheetah!'
all the fans scream out and clap
as he streaks right past the finish line
and does an extra lap.

Then the Greyhound-cheetah anthem
is played loudly by the band
as the gold medal's presented
to him on the winners' stand.

'What's your secret?' the fans ask him,
'Could it be your daily feed?'
'Well,' he answers with a little bark,
'I guess I'm built for speed.'

And once the Games are over,
all the cheers and tears and fuss,
he takes his wife and cubs back home
on the Greyhound-cheetah bus.

Werrawi ... (Wagtail-kites)

Birdwatchers out on field trips
and game hunters on safari
bring back reports of strange white birds the tribesfolk
  call 'Werrawi'.

Werrawi? – Why?
'cos of their cry!

You see, each season when these flocks of
  wagtail-kites migrate,
they go off course
and lose their way and get into a state.

In puzzlement they circle round
flapping their wings in fear
and crying loudly, *Where are we?'* ... hoping someone
  will hear.

The tribesmen in the area
point up into the sky
and shout, 'It's the *Werrawi* – the *Werrawi* flying by!'

'Where are we? Oh, where are we?'
the birds cry in agitation,
for all they want to do is carry on with their migration.

'Werrawi,' shout the tribesmen,
waving palm leaves down below,
'if you stop crying *'Werrawi!'* – we will show you where to go.'

Then as they point towards the south,
the flocks, without delay,
jet off in fine formation, crying, 'Thanks – *We're on our way!'*

Froggymole

The froggymole lives underground
to stay away from light.
'My eyes get very sore,' he croaks, 'when the sun's rays
   are too bright.'

To save his bulgy froggy eyes
and shield them from the glare,
he buys at the optometrist dark sunglasses to wear.

Each morning when he wakes up
froggymole jumps out of bed,
hops over to his porthole and pops out his small mole-head.

And if the day looks sunny
he is not at all distressed,
washes, and brushes mole-ar teeth and rushes to get dressed.

'A perfect day for golf,' he laughs,
'and good for froggymoles.
I'll tunnel up to watch the golfers play their 18 holes.

'When wearing my sunglasses
I can follow while they play,
and when balls land up on mole-hills, I'll hop off
   and hide away.'

Though he irritates the golfers,
froggymole's a happy chap,
for when he has his glasses on – he's got no handicap!

A cheerful soul
is froggymole.

Author's Acknowledgements

Most projects involve many players. Some provide inspiration, some act as catalysts, some give encouragement, guidance and help and some are partners in the effort. This book is a perfect example.

The inspiration came from a collaboration with my son Norman about 30 years ago, when we had a lot of fun making up a rhyme for one of his school projects. That was the original Ambervulturecrocs. So thanks, Norm. Then, when I was visiting Norman and his family in New York a couple of years ago, we had a few laughs trying to remember the rhyme, which ended up with my creating a few more crazy mixed-up animals with his daughters, Noa and Shira.

Back in Cape Town, the next major player was my daughter Lisa, who showed the rhymes to a friend in the publishing world. To my surprise, she liked them, and enter publishing manager, Linda de Villiers, who provided the spur for me to create the rest of the animals.

Encouragement came primarily from Lisa, my husband Noah, my sister-in-law Hilda, and daughters Robinne and Jodi, all of whom were subjected to repeated readings as, over many months, I honed the forty two 'weird and wonderful' creatures, each of which took on a definite identity and personality. We even found ourselves becoming quite attached to them.

Once the rhymes were completed, two other special women entered the picture – my editor, Irma van Wyk and designer, Bev Dodd. To them, and to Linda de Villiers, goes my greatest admiration and appreciation. They were absolutely great – helpful, considerate and utterly professional. It was a pleasure to work with them.

Finally, I thank illustrator Tony Grogan, who brought all my funny animal friends to life more brilliantly than I could ever have imagined. He's a genius!

And in a post script, acknowledging my Latin teaching background, somewhere lurking in my mind I may well have been inspired by that well-known line – *Ex Africa semper aliquid novi* – out of Africa there's always something new. This book is confirmation.

First published in 2005 by Struik Publishers
(a division of New Holland Publishing
(South Africa) (Pty) Ltd)
Cornelis Struik House, 80 McKenzie Street,
Cape Town 8001
86–88 Edgware Road, London,
W2 2EA, United Kingdom
14 Aquatic Drive, Frenchs Forest,
NSW 2086, Australia
218 Lake Road, Northcote, Auckland,
New Zealand

New Holland Publishing is a member of
Johnnic Communications Ltd

www.struik.co.za

PUBLISHING MANAGER: Linda de Villiers
MANAGING EDITOR: Cecilia Barfield
EDITOR: Irma van Wyk
DESIGNER: Beverley Dodd
ILLUSTRATOR: Tony Grogan
PROOFREADER: Samantha Fick

Reproduction by Hirt & Carter Cape (Pty) Ltd
Printed and bound by Sing Cheong Printing
Company Limited, Hong Kong

ISBN 1 77007 164 4

IMAGES OF AFRICA
PHOTO LIBRARY